MW00654886

FREE to be ME!

As I **emerged** from the cocooned chrysalis that held me captive,
I realized how **awesome** it felt to be free - **Blessed** to be me.

With all my **passion**, and purpose I morphed into a woman grounded
in her **faith** who **believes** she can be - Whatever she desires to be.

So, with deep **gratitude** for the **love** and **grace** I've extended to me
I breathe in my presence with **great joy** - Because I am finally **free**

Free to be ME!

This Notebook Belongs to:

Made in the USA
Columbia, SC
07 February 2021